TRUE WAR STORIES

PERSONAL ACCOUNTS OF HISTORY'S GREATEST CONFLICTS

An Imprint of Sterling Publishing
387 Park Avenue South
New York, NY 10016

Text © 2013 by Capstone Publishers
Illustrations © 2013 by Capstone Publishers
Chris Harbo, Editor • Ashlee Suker, Designer

This 2014 edition published by Sandy Creek.

ISBN 978-1-4351-5432-2

Printed and bound in Shenzhen, China.
Lot #:
2 4 6 8 10 9 7 5 3 1
03/14

TABLE OF CONTENTS

True Stories of the REVOLUTIONARY WAR

by Elizabeth Raum

illustrated by Pat Kinsella

THE AMERICAN REVOLUTION: A WAR FOR INDEPENDENCE

Since the founding of Jamestown, Virginia, in 1607, Great Britain ruled much of colonial America. And for more than 150 years, life was generally good. Most colonists considered themselves British. They spoke English, practiced British manners, and traded with Great Britain.

During the 1750s, war broke out between France and Great Britain. The French and Indian War (1754–1763) left Great Britain in need of money. King George III forced American colonists to pay new taxes to cover the war costs. The Stamp Act, passed in 1765, taxed most printed materials, including newspapers, stamps, and even playing cards. Many colonists refused to pay. They thought it unfair that they should have to pay these taxes, yet have no direct say in their government. Eventually the Stamp Act was overturned. Colonists also decided to boycott, or stop buying, British products, such as tea. When a large shipment of tea arrived in Boston Harbor, tempers flared. Angry colonists in Boston snuck onto the three tea ships one night and dumped 90,000 pounds (40,820 kilograms) of tea into Boston Harbor.

Anger rose quickly throughout the colonies. Fighting broke out between the colonists and British soldiers on April 19, 1775, at Lexington and Concord, Massachusetts. A little more than a year later, on July 4, 1776, the colonies declared their independence from Great Britain.

More than 200,000 colonists fought in the Revolutionary War. Unlike the British soldiers, many were woefully untrained. They often lacked guns, ammunition, and other basic supplies. But despite the odds, after eight long years, the patriots won their freedom.

Throughout the war, people wrote letters and kept diaries and journals about their daily lives. Thanks to the writings of the six men and women in this book, you can hear the cries of battle. You can smell the gunpowder, and feel the fear and bravery inside the true stories of the Revolutionary War.

Key Dates of the Revolutionary War

APRIL 1775: Shots are fired at Lexington and Concord (Massachusetts).

JUNE 1775: The Battle of Bunker Hill (Breeds Hill; Massachusetts) is the first battle of the Revolutionary War.

JULY 4, 1776: The Continental Congress adopts the Declaration of Independence.

AUGUST 1776: The British win the Battle of Long Island (New York).

SEPTEMBER – OCTOBER 1777: The Battles at Saratoga (New York) strengthen the Continental army's confidence.

DECEMBER 1777: The Continental army reaches Valley Forge (Pennsylvania).

APRIL 1780: The British win the Battle of Monck's Corner (South Carolina).

MARCH 15, 1781: The British win the Battle of Guilford Courthouse (North Carolina).

SEPTEMBER – OCTOBER 1781: The Continental army wins the Battle of Yorktown (Virginia), the final major land battle of the war.

FEBRUARY 14, 1783: Great Britain officially declares an end to the war.

SEPTEMBER 3, 1783: The United States and Great Britain sign the Treaty of Paris.

AMERICAN COLONIES IN 1775

Legend:
- NEW ENGLAND COLONIES
- MIDDLE COLONIES
- SOUTHERN COLONIES

MASSACHUSETTS
NEW HAMPSHIRE
RHODE ISLAND
CONNECTICUT

NEW YORK
PENNSYLVANIA
NEW JERSEY
MARYLAND
DELAWARE
VIRGINIA
NORTH CAROLINA
SOUTH CAROLINA
GEORGIA

Atlantic Ocean

N

0   100   200 miles

0   100   200 kilometers

Revolutionary War Stories

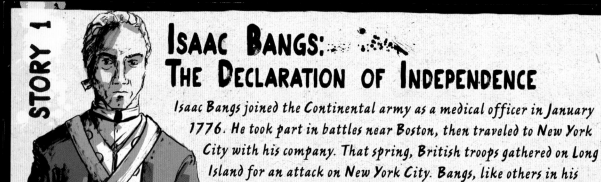

STORY 1

ISAAC BANGS:
THE DECLARATION OF INDEPENDENCE

Isaac Bangs joined the Continental army as a medical officer in January 1776. He took part in battles near Boston, then traveled to New York City with his company. That spring, British troops gathered on Long Island for an attack on New York City. Bangs, like others in his company, waited anxiously for a signal for the fighting to begin.

July 6, 1776

In a tavern in New York City ...

What news, gentlemen?

Congress declared the United Colonies free and independent from Britain!

Huzzah!

General Washington has ordered that the Declaration of Independence be read aloud to the troops three days from now. Be sure to gather your men.

Did you see the crowd topple King George's statue last night?

Yes. General Washington ordered it to be melted down and made into ammunition for our guns.

Perhaps those bullets will make an impression on some of King George's Redcoats.

Ha! Ha!

A short time later, Lieutenant Bangs left the Continental army and joined the Navy. He died in 1780 while serving as a surgeon. He didn't live long enough to see the colonies win the war for independence.

REDCOATS

American colonists called British soldiers *Redcoats* because they wore bright red coats and white breeches (short pants). General Washington and his officers wore deep blue coats and buff-colored breeches. Every regiment designed its own special coat buttons.

FREDERIKA VON RIEDESEL: THE BATTLE OF FREEMAN'S FARM

In 1777 Baroness Frederika von Riedesel came to America from Germany. Her husband, a German general commanded German soldiers fighting with the British. Frederika brought along three young daughters and several servants. They joined General von Riedesel in Canada and began following the British army south through New York.

September 11, 1777

Where are we?

Near Saratoga. We've seized this house from the Americans. You and the other women will stay here.

Where are you going?

To battle.

Will it never stop?

About a week later, the Battle of Freeman's Farm began.

LYDIA DARRAGH:
SPYING IN PHILADELPHIA

Lydia Darragh lived in Philadelphia with her husband, William. They belonged to a religious group called the Society of Friends, or Quakers. Quakers did not believe in warfare, and most Quakers remained neutral during the Revolutionary War. They didn't take sides.

Lydia, however, favored independence. She kept her feelings secret.

Late fall 1777

The British commander, General William Howe, took a house across the street from us as his headquarters. He wanted to take our house, too, for secret meetings. I had to convince him not to.

Captain Barrington? From Ireland?

Cousin Lydia?

How are you? Do you have business with General Howe?

Oh, dear cousin. The general wishes to throw us out of our home!

Let me talk to him and see what I can do.

Late night, December 2, 1777

To my relief, General Howe agreed to use just one room of our home. We were to be asleep during the meetings. But I listened.

My eldest son had broken with Quaker tradition and joined the Continental army.

On December 4, we attack Washington's troops here, at White Marsh. We'll take them by surprise.

He was now in harm's way. I knew spying was dangerous, but I had to protect my family.

They'll never know what hit them.

I listened as long as I could. Then I rushed to my room and pretended to sleep.

After picking up the flour, I stopped at the Rising Sun Tavern. I knew that the Continental army picked up information there.

I was so nervous, I nearly fainted.

Please, sir, deliver this to General Washington as soon as possible.

So, General Howe is planning a surprise for us? We'll see about that.

Thankfully, my message reached General Washington. His men were able to prepare themselves for the attack.

The British continued using Lydia Darragh's home for their meetings. They never discovered that she was a spy. Three years after her husband's death in 1786, Lydia moved to another home. She ran a store until she died in 1789, at age 61.

ALBIGENCE WALDO: THE BATTLE OF WHITE MARSH

On July 6, 1775, Albigence Waldo became a surgeon's mate in a Connecticut regiment. Like most doctors of the time, he had learned medicine by studying with another doctor. In September 1777 Waldo's regiment joined General George Washington at White Marsh, about 13 miles (21 kilometers) northwest of Philadelphia, Pennsylvania.

December 1, 1777

My regiment had no tents at White Marsh. So we built huts of sticks and leaves to shelter ourselves from the cold, stormy weather.

December 2, 1777

We knew the British were approaching. But we didn't know when they'd arrive.

Sharpen those sticks!

This should stop the Redcoats.

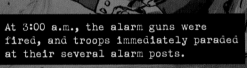

STORY 5

LIEUTENANT ANTHONY ALLAIRE: THE BATTLE OF MONCK'S CORNER

Anthony Allaire was a lieutenant in the Loyal American Volunteers. This company remained loyal to King George III and fought with the British against George Washington's forces. Allaire became the assistant to British colonel Patrick Ferguson, and went with him to South Carolina to fight the rebels.

April 13, 1780

Our calvary unit had just marched 22 miles (35 km) and gotten less than two hours of sleep when we received our next orders.

Look lively, men! We're heading to Goose Creek to meet up with Lieutenant Tarleton. Charleston is within reach!

When we arrived, Lieutenant Tarleton showed us a letter.

My men captured this from a messenger. It has all the information we need to plan our attack.

No time for rest. The Americans are camped at Monck's Corner. We'll march through the night and surprise them at dawn.

How did we do?

We took 30 wagons, with four horses each. A number of fine horses that belonged to their troops were likewise taken.

The Battle of Monck's Corner was an important British victory. Without a way to communicate with the rest of the rebel forces, the city of Charleston was forced to surrender to the British on May 12, 1780. Anthony Allaire fled to Canada in 1783.

LOYALISTS

Those who remained loyal to Great Britain during the Revolutionary War were called Loyalists, Tories, or King's Men. They felt the colonies were safer under British protection, and they wanted to continue trading with Great Britain. About one-fifth of the colonists were loyalists. After the war, many left for England. Others went to Canada or other British colonies.

31

SARAH OSBORN BENJAMIN: THE BATTLE OF YORKTOWN

Sarah Osborn Benjamin was a camp follower—a woman who followed her husband to war. She cooked, washed, and sewed for the soldiers in her husband's New York regiment. In September 1781 Sarah followed the Continental army from West Point, New York, to Yorktown, Virginia. It would be her final taste of battle.

October 1781

It was quite a sight, that large plain separating us from Yorktown. The British held the city. And our men were determined to take it back.

We women did our best behind the lines.

Fighting men are hungry men.

British General Charles Cornwallis surrendered to the Continentals on October 19, 1781. With the war over, Sarah, her husband, and the rest of the regiment returned to New York. Sarah didn't share her battlefield stories with anyone until 1837, when she was 81.

WOMEN IN THE REVOLUTIONARY WAR

Camp followers, like Sarah Osborn Benjamin and Frederika von Riedesel, spent the Revolutionary War near the battlefield with the men. Many of the women were soldiers' wives. However, most women in the colonies stayed home. They took on the difficult tasks of managing families, farms, and businesses while their husbands were at war.

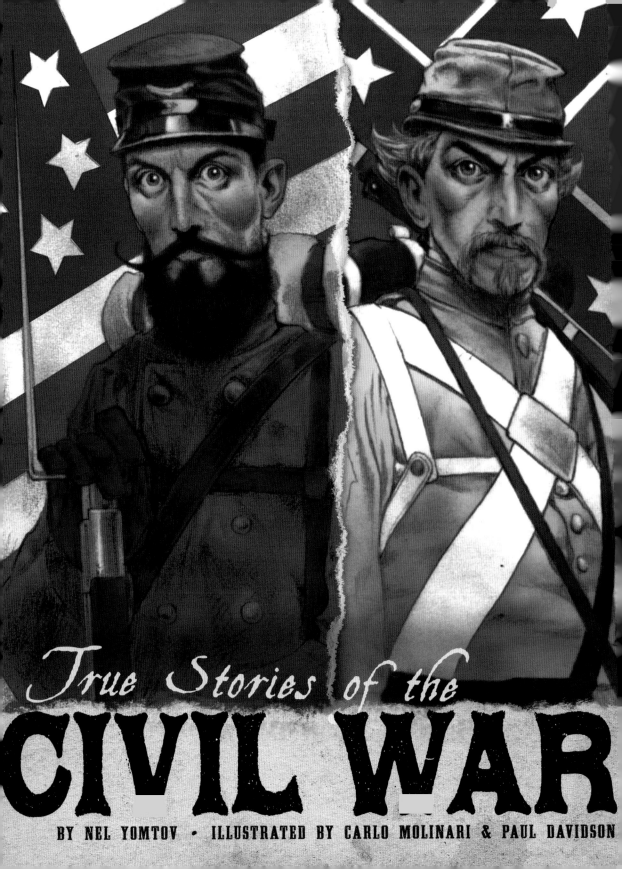

True Stories of the
CIVIL WAR

BY NEL YOMTOV · ILLUSTRATED BY CARLO MOLINARI & PAUL DAVIDSON

THE U.S. CIVIL WAR: A NATION TORN

The U.S. Civil War (1861–1865) was by far the deadliest conflict in U.S. history. And it nearly destroyed the young nation.

The road to war was paved with many disagreements between the Northern and Southern states. One of the biggest disagreements was over slavery. The South's economy depended on farming and slave labor. In the North, however, slavery was illegal. Many Northerners did not want new states joining the Union to be allowed to have slaves. Southerners worried that if the federal government became too strong, it would outlaw slavery everywhere. They feared that their way of life would be shattered. As the years passed, anger grew.

The South reached its breaking point when Abraham Lincoln was elected president in November 1860. Because of his strong support in the North, Southerners feared Lincoln would end slavery. Within weeks South Carolina withdrew, or seceded, from the Union. More Southern states soon followed. In February 1861 these states formed a new and independent government called the Confederate States of America (CSA), or the Confederacy.

On April 12, 1861, Confederate forces struck. They shelled the Union's Fort Sumter in South Carolina. Two days later Union forces inside the fort were forced to surrender. The Civil War had begun.

After four long years, the Union won the war. More than 620,000 Americans died from fighting and disease. Roughly 400,000 were wounded. Join six brave soldiers as they take you through the darkest, bloodiest war in U.S. history.

Key Dates of the Civil War

APRIL 12, 1861: The war begins when Confederate forces attack the Union's Fort Sumter in South Carolina.

JULY 21, 1861: Confederate troops win the First Battle of Bull Run in Manassas, Virginia.

MARCH 9, 1862: The battle between the Union *Monitor* and the Confederate *Merrimac* ends in a draw.

APRIL 6–7, 1862: Union troops win the Battle of Shiloh in Tennessee.

SEPTEMBER 17, 1862: Union troops win the Battle of Antietam in Sharpsburg, Maryland.

MAY 1–4, 1863: Confederate forces claim victory at the Battle of Chancellorsville in Virginia.

JULY 1–3, 1863: Union troops win the Battle of Gettysburg in Pennsylvania.

MAY 5–7, 1864: The Battle of the Wilderness in Virginia ends in a draw.

APRIL 9, 1865: General Robert E. Lee surrenders to the Union army, ending the Civil War.

CANADA

MINNESOTA

DAKOTA
TERRITORY

WISCONSIN

Lake Superior

MICHIGAN

Lake Michigan

Lake Huron

Lake Ontario

MAINE

VERMONT

NEW HAMPSHIRE

NEW YORK

MASSACHUSETTS

RHODE ISLAND
CONNECTICUT

Lake Erie

PENNSYLVANIA

NEW JERSEY

NEBRASKA
TERRITORY

IOWA

ILLINOIS

INDIANA

OHIO

DELAWARE

MARYLAND

KANSAS

MISSOURI

KENTUCKY

VIRGINIA

UNORGANIZED
TERRITORY

ARKANSAS

TENNESSEE

NORTH
CAROLINA

SOUTH
CAROLINA

N
W E
S

TEXAS

MISSISSIPPI

ALABAMA

GEORGIA

LOUISIANA

FLORIDA

0   100   200   300 miles

0   100 200 300 kilometers

UNION STATES, 1861
CONFEDERATE STATES, 1861
TERRITORIES

Atlantic Ocean

Gulf of Mexico

39

CIVIL WAR STORIES

STEPHEN LEE: THE ATTACK ON FORT SUMTER

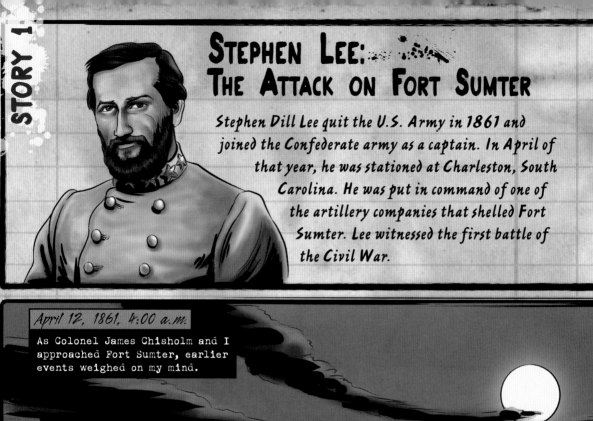

Stephen Dill Lee quit the U.S. Army in 1861 and joined the Confederate army as a captain. In April of that year, he was stationed at Charleston, South Carolina. He was put in command of one of the artillery companies that shelled Fort Sumter. Lee witnessed the first battle of the Civil War.

April 12, 1861, 4:00 a.m.

As Colonel James Chisholm and I approached Fort Sumter, earlier events weighed on my mind.

I had delivered a message to Major Robert Anderson, the commander of the fort. The message stated that our batteries in Charleston Harbor would fire upon the fort.

This is a sad day for our nation, Colonel Chisholm.

Indeed it is. Let's hope this is over and done with quickly.

We were there to witness the firing of the "first gun of the war" between the States.

The firing of the shell was a success. It burst immediately over the fort, apparently 100 feet above.

The firing of the mortar brought every soldier in the harbor to his feet, and every man, woman, and child in the city of Charleston from their beds.

Look, Pa!

Fetch your mother and sisters. I want them to see this!

The first shot was the signal for our forts to open fire on Sumter.

A thrill went through the whole city. No one thought of going home.

They've come from every nook and corner to see this, sir!

7:00 a.m.

When Union forces returned fire, Major Anderson avoided using his best guns. They sat in positions that would expose his men to direct shelling.

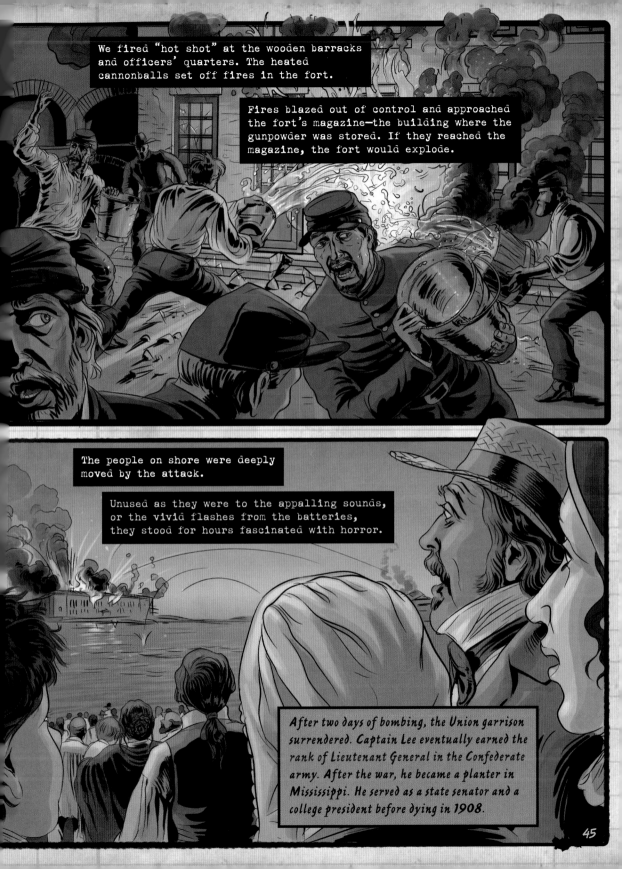

We fired "hot shot" at the wooden barracks and officers' quarters. The heated cannonballs set off fires in the fort.

Fires blazed out of control and approached the fort's magazine—the building where the gunpowder was stored. If they reached the magazine, the fort would explode.

The people on shore were deeply moved by the attack.

Unused as they were to the appalling sounds, or the vivid flashes from the batteries, they stood for hours fascinated with horror.

After two days of bombing, the Union garrison surrendered. Captain Lee eventually earned the rank of Lieutenant General in the Confederate army. After the war, he became a planter in Mississippi. He served as a state senator and a college president before dying in 1908.

SAMUEL ENGLISH: THE BATTLE OF THE FIRST BULL RU

Samuel J. English was a corporal in Company D of the Second Rhode Island Volunteers. On the evening of July 18, 1861, Union troops made camp along a stream known as Bull Run, in Virginia. A short distance away, Confederate forces guarded an important railroad junction. The scene was set for the first major conflict of the Civil War.

July 21, 1861, 2:00 a.m.

About two o'clock the drums beat assembly. In 10 minutes we were on our march for Bull Run, having heard the enemy was waiting to receive us.

RAT-TA-TAT RAT-TA-TAT RAT-TA-TAT

C'mon, boys. That's the sound you've been waiting for. Move out!

Is it r-really time to g-go, Corporal English? W-we've been camped here only three days.

You'll be fine. Just stay with the regiment.

Our regiments were ordered off the field. When our line had formed again, I started off to see how the fight was progressing.

I passed the farm house which had been appropriated for a hospital. The groans of the wounded and dying men were horrible.

YEE-AAY-EEE   YEE-AAY-EEE

Soon hundreds of additional Confederate soldiers arrived and attacked our lines.

They let out a howling sound that became known as the "rebel yell."

The enemy is upon us! Retreat!

My men fought hard. But when the call to retreat sounded, no one knew what to do or where to go. They simply hadn't had enough training.

The stampede became frightful.

The rebels mowed down our men like grass.

... I started up the hill as fast as my legs could carry.

We kept on to Washington where we arrived about two o'clock on Monday, more dead than alive.

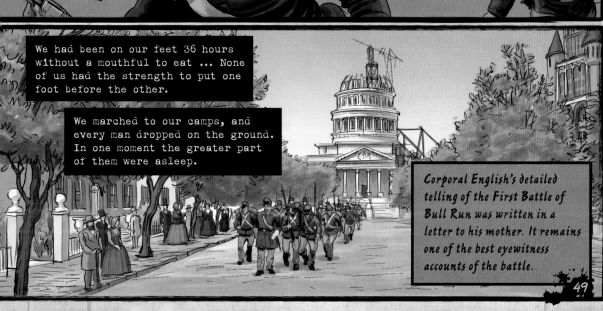

We had been on our feet 36 hours without a mouthful to eat ... None of us had the strength to put one foot before the other.

We marched to our camps, and every man dropped on the ground. In one moment the greater part of them were asleep.

Corporal English's detailed telling of the First Battle of Bull Run was written in a letter to his mother. It remains one of the best eyewitness accounts of the battle.

49

SAMUEL DANA GREENE: BATTLE OF THE IRONCLADS

Samuel Dana Greene graduated from the U.S. Naval Academy in 1859. In 1862 he became executive officer of the USS Monitor, the Union's new ironclad ship. It was the navy's last and only hope against the Confederate ironclad Merrimac, which had recently begun destroying Union wooden ships. If Greene and the Monitor couldn't stop the Merrimac, the Union navy would be doomed.

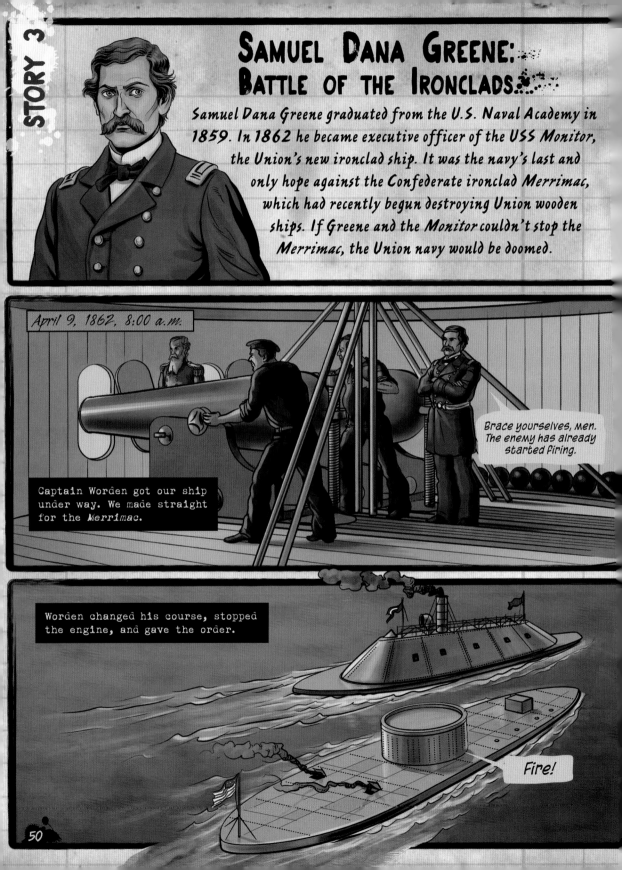

April 9, 1862, 8:00 a.m.

Captain Worden got our ship under way. We made straight for the *Merrimac*.

Brace yourselves, men. The enemy has already started firing.

Worden changed his course, stopped the engine, and gave the order.

Fire!

Our turret turned fiercely hot and filled with smoke. The *Merrimac*'s cannonballs slammed into our iron plates. The sound echoed painfully in our ears.

The *Merrimac* tried to ram us. But Worden avoided the direct impact, and she struck only a glancing blow that did no damage.

Soon after noon, a shell from the enemy's gun struck the forward side of the pilothouse. It hit directly in the sight-hole, or slit, and exploded.

Captain Worden was standing immediately behind this spot. He received in his face the force of the blow, which utterly blinded him.

AGGH!

Take command of the Monitor, Greene.

Yes, Captain. Let's get you to safer quarters.

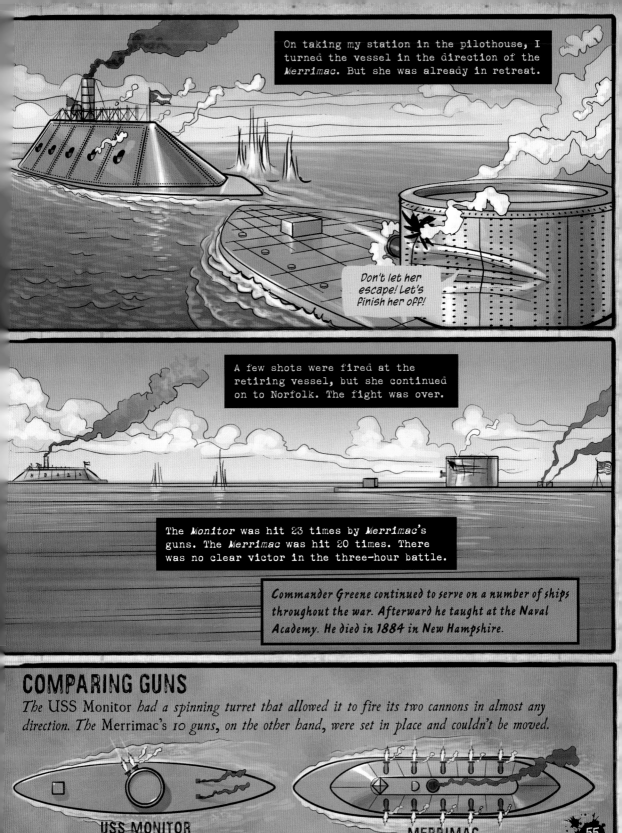

On taking my station in the pilothouse, I turned the vessel in the direction of the *Merrimac*. But she was already in retreat.

Don't let her escape! Let's finish her off!

A few shots were fired at the retiring vessel, but she continued on to Norfolk. The fight was over.

The *Monitor* was hit 23 times by *Merrimac's* guns. The *Merrimac* was hit 20 times. There was no clear victor in the three-hour battle.

Commander Greene continued to serve on a number of ships throughout the war. Afterward he taught at the Naval Academy. He died in 1884 in New Hampshire.

COMPARING GUNS

The USS Monitor *had a spinning turret that allowed it to fire its two cannons in almost any direction. The* Merrimac's *10 guns, on the other hand, were set in place and couldn't be moved.*

USS MONITOR

MERRIMAC

DAVID THOMPSON: THE BATTLE OF ANTIETAM

David Ludlow Thompson was a private in Company G, 9th Regiment, New York Volunteers. On September 17, 1862, the opening shots of the Battle of Antietam, in Maryland, were fired. A bloody struggle followed. It started in Miller's cornfield and ended at the Stone Bridge over Antietam Creek. Private Thompson and his regiment were positioned there.

September 17, 1862

At 10 o'clock in the morning, General Burnside ordered troops to cross the bridge. But they were quickly mowed down in a hail of gunfire. Now, at noon, my regiment and I waited for our orders.

It's our turn up, Thompson.

Good luck to you, Dodson. See you on the other side!

A silence fell on everyone at once, for each felt the momentous "now" had come.

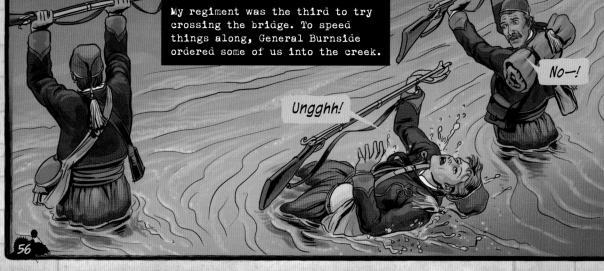

My regiment was the third to try crossing the bridge. To speed things along, General Burnside ordered some of us into the creek.

No—!

Ungghh!

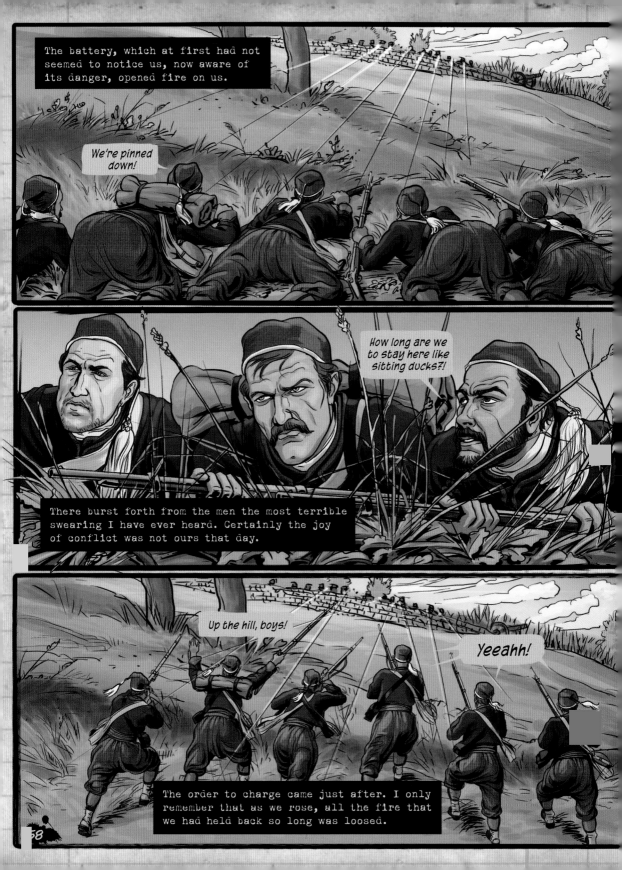

In a second the air was full of the hiss of bullets and the hurtle of cannon shot.

The rebels wilted under our charge and fled the battlefield.

Minutes later ...

It seemed to be all over in a moment. Our sergeant-major called me to unroll my blanket and help to carry from the field one of our wounded lieutenants.

Private Thompson's time at Antietam Creek was not over. He was captured by Confederate forces later that evening and held prisoner for nine days. He was later exchanged for Confederate prisoners held by Union forces.

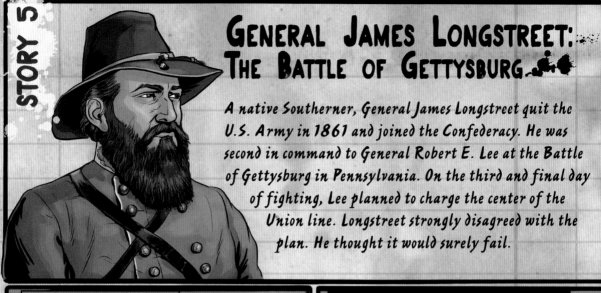

GENERAL JAMES LONGSTREET: THE BATTLE OF GETTYSBURG

A native Southerner, General James Longstreet quit the U.S. Army in 1861 and joined the Confederacy. He was second in command to General Robert E. Lee at the Battle of Gettysburg in Pennsylvania. On the third and final day of fighting, Lee planned to charge the center of the Union line. Longstreet strongly disagreed with the plan. He thought it would surely fail.

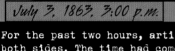

July 3, 1863, 3:00 p.m.

For the past two hours, artillery blasted from both sides. The time had come. Major General George Pickett looked to me for his orders.

Shall I advance, General Longstreet?

I couldn't speak. I knew a frontal attack on the Union army was doomed. All I could do was bow my "yes."

I shall lead my division forward, sir.

Hurry on, men!

Step lively!

We're going to crush those Yanks!

When our troops were within 250 yards of the enemy's line, every Union rifle blazed.

Soldiers and officers began to fall, some to rise no more ... But the grand march moved bravely on.

The day is done, boys. The fight is over.

Despite their heroism, our troops were doomed to failure. They were no match for the Union's rifles. It was, quite simply, a bloodbath.

General Pickett ... called the troops off. The broken lines marched back in steady step.

You've served the South well! I'm proud of you all!

Roughly 6,500 Confederates were killed or wounded in Pickett's Charge. The Confederates fled south and never tried to invade Northern territory again.

General Longstreet continued to serve as General Lee's "old war-horse" until the end of the war. He later worked for the U.S. government and wrote a memoir of his battle experiences. He lived to the age of 82.

WOMEN SOLDIERS

Most women helped the war effort by providing supplies and offering whatever support they could. A few women, however, hid their true selves in order to serve in the Union and Confederate armies. They often cut their hair short and wore men's clothing when they went to sign up. Some women avoided the official process and joined a unit right before a battle.

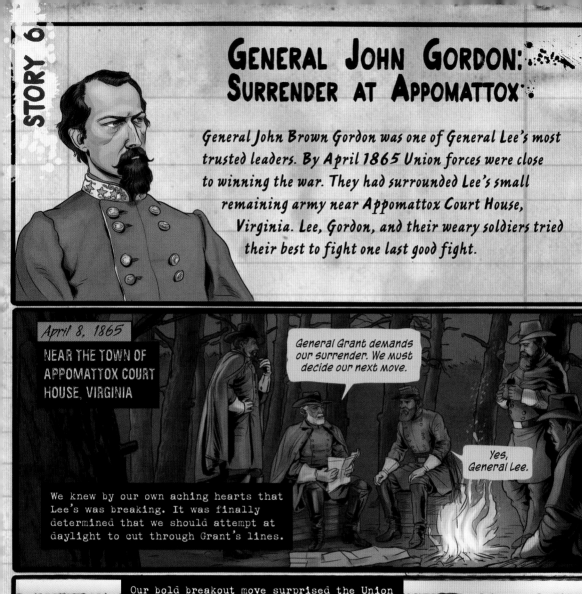

GENERAL JOHN GORDON:
SURRENDER AT APPOMATTOX

General John Brown Gordon was one of General Lee's most trusted leaders. By April 1865 Union forces were close to winning the war. They had surrounded Lee's small remaining army near Appomattox Court House, Virginia. Lee, Gordon, and their weary soldiers tried their best to fight one last good fight.

April 8, 1865

NEAR THE TOWN OF APPOMATTOX COURT HOUSE, VIRGINIA

General Grant demands our surrender. We must decide our next move.

Yes, General Lee.

We knew by our own aching hearts that Lee's was breaking. It was finally determined that we should attempt at daylight to cut through Grant's lines.

Our bold breakout move surprised the Union troops, but soon we were overpowered.

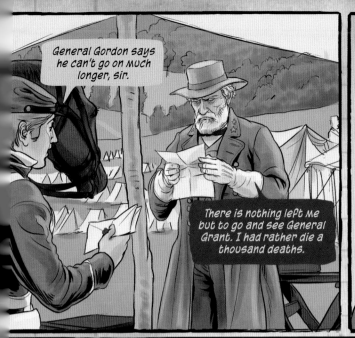

General Gordon says he can't go on much longer, sir.

There is nothing left me but to go and see General Grant. I had rather die a thousand deaths.

My troops were still furiously fighting ... when the note from General Lee reached me. It notified me that there was a flag of truce between Grant and himself, and that hostilities would stop.

April 9, 1865

General, are we surrendered?

Yes, son. We have fought the war together, and I have done the best I could for you.

The men could no longer control their emotions, and tears ran like water down their shrunken faces.

General Gordon went on to a successful career in politics following the war. He served as a senator and governor for Georgia, and was very active with veterans' groups. He died in 1904.

True Stories of
WORLD
WAR I

BY NEL YOMTOV

ILLUSTRATED BY
JON PROCTOR

WORLD WAR I: THE GREAT WAR

Even for people who didn't live through it, World War I (1914–1918) is known as the Great War. Never before had two alliances of the world's most powerful nations clashed in mortal combat. The Allied powers included Great Britain, France, Russia, Belgium, and later the United States. The Central powers mainly included Germany, Austria-Hungary, and the Ottoman Empire.

The assassination of Archduke Franz Ferdinand by a Bosnian-Serb in June 1914 sparked the conflict. Ferdinand was in line for the Austria-Hungary throne. The shooter was a member of a revolutionary movement. He wanted the Serbian people to form a nation independent from Austria-Hungary.

One month later, the flames of war erupted in full. Austria-Hungary invaded Serbia. Germany then invaded Belgium, Luxembourg, and France. Russia attacked Germany. Fighting then broke out in Italy, Bulgaria, Romania, and in Pacific Ocean territories. For years the United States tried to stay out of the war. But in 1917 Germany's attacks on American commercial ships bound for Britain could not be ignored. The United States joined the war.

In November 1918 Germany, the only remaining Central power left fighting, agreed to a cease-fire. After four years of bloody combat, more than 35 million soldiers and civilians were dead, wounded, or missing.

Many soldiers kept diaries and journals about their experiences during the war. Get ready to explore six personal accounts of brave soldiers from both sides of the conflict.

KEY DATES OF WORLD WAR I

JUNE 1914: Archduke Franz Ferdinand is assassinated.

AUGUST 1914: Germany declares war on France and Belgium. Britain declares war on Germany. Austria-Hungary declares war on Russia.

SEPTEMBER 1914: Allied forces win the First Battle of the Marne near Paris, France.

OCTOBER-NOVEMBER 1914: Allied forces win the First Battle of Ypres in Belgium.

MAY 1915: A German U-boat sinks the British passenger liner Lusitania, killing 1,198 civilians.

APRIL 1915-MAY 1916: The Central powers win the Gallipoli Campaign in Turkey.

FEBRUARY-DECEMBER 1916: Allied forces win the Battle of Verdun in France.

JULY-NOVEMBER 1916: The Battle of the Somme is fought to a draw in France.

APRIL 1917: The United States declares war on Germany.

JULY-AUGUST 1918: Allied forces win the Second Battle of the Marne in France.

NOVEMBER 1918: Germany agrees to a cease-fire, ending the war.

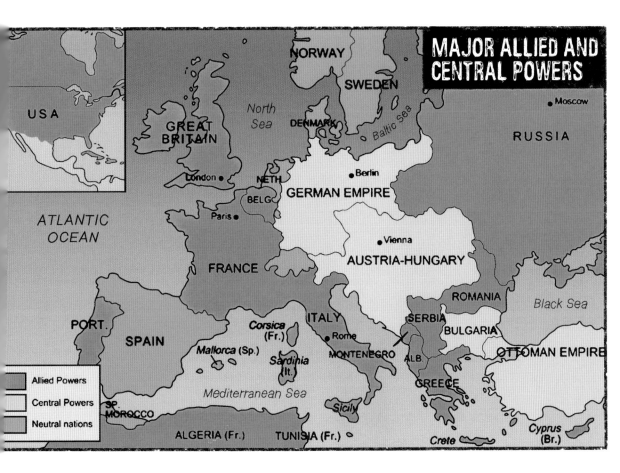

MAJOR ALLIED AND CENTRAL POWERS

USA

NORWAY

SWEDEN

North Sea

DENMARK

Baltic Sea

• Moscow

GREAT BRITAIN

RUSSIA

London •

NETH.

• Berlin

ATLANTIC OCEAN

BELG.

GERMAN EMPIRE

Paris •

FRANCE

• Vienna

AUSTRIA-HUNGARY

ROMANIA

Black Sea

PORT.

ITALY

SERBIA

BULGARIA

SPAIN

Corsica (Fr.)

• Rome

Mallorca (Sp.)

Sardinia (It.)

MONTENEGRO

ALB.

OTTOMAN EMPIRE

Mediterranean Sea

GREECE

SP. MOROCCO

Sicily

Cyprus (Br.)

ALGERIA (Fr.)

TUNISIA (Fr.)

Crete

Allied Powers

Central Powers

Neutral nations

WORLD WAR I STORIES

But the men didn't complain. They knew holding these trenches was an honor.

They buckled down and did their duty together.

Their minds were full of the folk at home whom they might not see again, and of the struggle that lay before them.

Here's one of my mum, Hankey. I miss her dearly.

You'll see her soon, Westie. I'm sure of it.

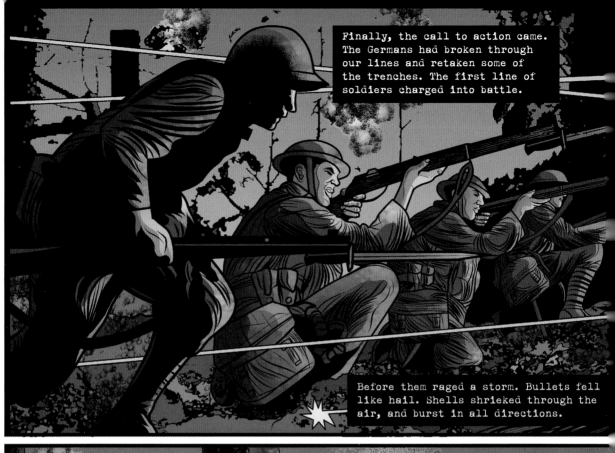

Finally, the call to action came. The Germans had broken through our lines and retaken some of the trenches. The first line of soldiers charged into battle.

Before them raged a storm. Bullets fell like hail. Shells shrieked through the air, and burst in all directions.

Suddenly, a whistle blew. Soldiers next to me scrambled to their feet and charged forward.

The brigade had had its baptism in blood, and its self-confidence was established for all time.

Donald Hankey tasted victory in his first battle, but he was wounded near Ypres, Belgium, in July 1915. He returned to action about one year later and was killed in combat in October 1916. He was buried where he fell near Le Tronsloy, France.

In his career, Captain Schwieger sunk 49 ships. On September 5, 1917, he was killed when his U-boat hit a British mine. His body was never recovered.

THE TIDE TURNS

The sinking of the *Lusitania* had a huge impact on the direction of *World War I*. At the time of its sinking, the *United States* was not yet fighting in the war. But the death of 1,198 people on an unarmed passenger ship outraged many Americans. The event turned public opinion against Germany. It fueled the *United States'* entrance into the war in 1917.

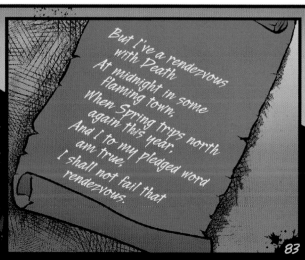

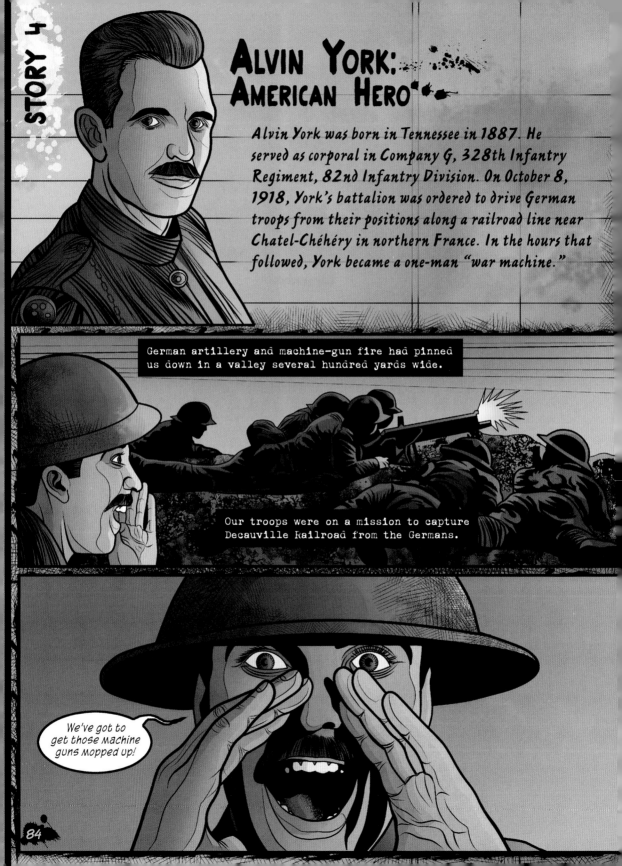

Suddenly, the machine guns on top of the hill swung around and opened fire.

The Germans couldn't miss. Our troops began dropping like flies.

Faster! Don't let them escape!

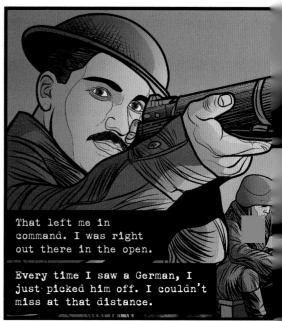

That left me in command. I was right out there in the open.

Every time I saw a German, I just picked him off. I couldn't miss at that distance.

In the middle of the fight, a German officer and five men ... charged me with fixed bayonets.

I flipped out my pistol and picked them off too.

Come on down and give up! I don't want to kill any more of you than I have to!

E-English?

No, not English. American.

I've already killed more than 20 of your men. Make them surrender, or you'll be next.

I will make them give up.

I'm taking you to the American lines. Just don't do anything stupid.

He blew a little whistle and they came down ... There were nearly 100 of them.

Keep hiking, major.

We still had the German front line to go through. I ordered the major to blow his whistle. More Germans surrendered and joined our march.

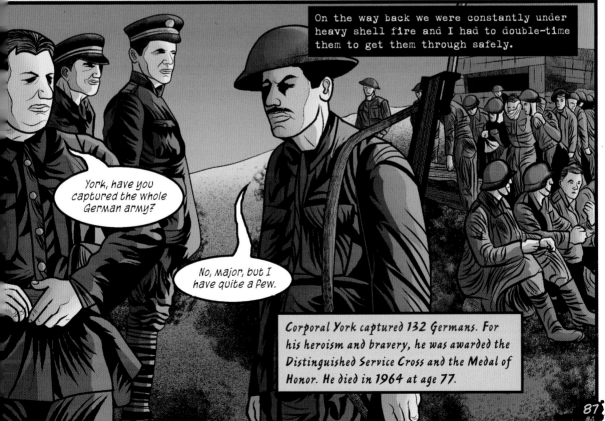

On the way back we were constantly under heavy shell fire and I had to double-time them to get them through safely.

York, have you captured the whole German army?

No, major, but I have quite a few.

Corporal York captured 132 Germans. For his heroism and bravery, he was awarded the Distinguished Service Cross and the Medal of Honor. He died in 1964 at age 77.

Later that day, the Red Baron looked for another kill.

You English boys can run, but you're no match for my speed. No one is.

Richthofen went after the British plane in the rear of the formation.

Your friends have left you. Now you're mine!

The British pilot banked his plane into a cloud, hoping to escape the deadly fire of the Red Baron.

Got him! Now to see where he lands.

Richthofen swooped down to see if he had killed the enemy pilot.

Whoa! That boy's still got some life in him!

RATT TATT TATT

Ha ha! He should count himself lucky to have escaped with his life!

Curse you, Red Baron!

Baron Richthofen's own luck ran out on *April 21, 1918*. He was shot down and killed in northern France by a Canadian pilot. His last word was said to be "*kaputt*." It means "broken" or "no longer working" in German.

W-what happened? I don't remember anything ...

You've been out for three hours, Empey. We thought you were dead!

You're lucky you put your spare helmet on.

You can't imagine how delicious this cool, fresh air feels in my lungs!

Shortly after this gas attack, Empey was wounded during an assault on German trenches. He was discharged from the army and returned to his home in New Jersey.

GAS WARFARE

Both sides used gas warfare in World War I. At first, cylinders filled with gas were placed along the front lines facing enemy trenches. The cylinders were opened, and winds carried the gas into enemy positions. Later, gas was put into artillery shells and shot at the enemy. Chlorine gas attacked the lungs, taking away the victim's ability to breathe. Mustard gas attacked the skin. It burned its victims, causing terrible blisters, incredible pain, and sometimes death.

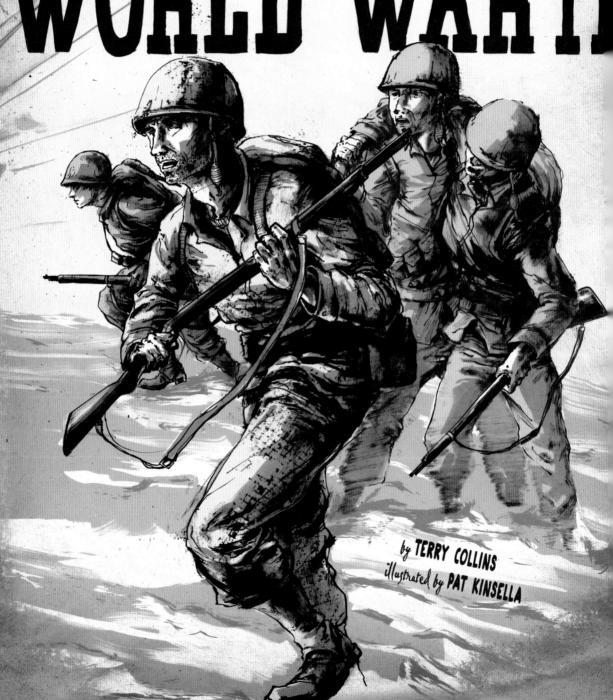

TRUE STORIES OF
WORLD WAR II

by TERRY COLLINS
illustrated by PAT KINSELLA

WORLD WAR II

After their defeat at the end of World War I (1914–1918), the German people's spirit was crushed. The country hungered for new leadership. In 1934 one man led the Nazi party to take over the German government. That man was Adolf Hitler.

Hitler's desire for power led him to declare war on Germany's neighboring countries. By the end of 1940, Germany had defeated France, Poland, Norway, the Netherlands, and Denmark. Germany then partnered with Italy and Japan to form the Axis powers. Their combined goal was to rule much of the world.

Meanwhile, Great Britain and the Soviet Union (USSR) joined forces with other countries. They created the Allied powers to battle the Axis. The United States stayed out of the fight at first. But Japan's attack on the U.S. naval base at Pearl Harbor in Hawaii on December 7, 1941, pushed the United States into the war.

World War II (1939–1945) lasted six years. By May 1945, Hitler's rule had collapsed and Germany surrendered to the Allies. In August the United States dropped two atomic bombs on Japan. This final act led to the surrender of Japan and the end of the war.

The Axis powers were broken, but the Allied victory was costly. The exact number of lives lost in the war, both soldier and civilian, will never be known. Historians estimate a body count between 50 and 70 million.

The leaders of the Allied forces are now household names: Franklin Delano Roosevelt, Joseph Stalin, Dwight D. Eisenhower, Winston Churchill, George S. Patton. But the war was fought and won by the courage of ordinary men and women. They were the true heroes of World War II. These are some of their stories.

KEY DATES OF WORLD WAR II

SEPTEMBER 1939: Hitler's forces invade Poland, starting World War II. Britain and France respond by declaring war on Germany.

JULY 1940: Germany begins bombing England.

JUNE 1941: Germany invades the Soviet Union.

DECEMBER 1941: Japan bombs the U.S. naval base at Pearl Harbor, Hawaii. The United States declares war on Japan.

JUNE 1942: Allied forces defeat Japan in the Battle of Midway.

SEPTEMBER 1943: Italy surrenders.

JUNE 6, 1944: Allied troops launch the massive D-day invasion of France.

MARCH 1945: Allied troops capture the island of Iwo Jima.

MAY 1945: Germany surrenders to the Allies.

AUGUST 1945: Atomic bombs code-named "Little Boy" and "Fat Man" dropped on the Japanese cities of Hiroshima and Nagasaki.

SEPTEMBER 1945: Japan surrenders, officially ending World War II.

ALLIED AND AXIS BOUNDARIES, 1939

SOVIET UNION

CHINA   JAPAN

PHILIPPINES   *Pacific
Ocean*

	Allied Controlled
	Axis Controlled
	Neutral

*Atlantic
Ocean*

SOVIET UNION

FINLAND

NORWAY   SWEDEN

ESTONIA

LATVIA

*North
Sea*   DENMARK

LITHUANIA

IRELAND

NETHERLANDS

PRUSSIA

GREAT
BRITAIN

POLAND

BELGIUM   GERMANY

SLOVAKIA

N

SWITZERLAND

W   E

FRANCE   HUNGARY

S   ROMANIA

ITALY   *Black Sea*

PORTUGAL   YUGOSLAVIA

BULGARIA

SPAIN   TURKEY

GREECE

SYRIA

WORLD WAR II STORIES

WILLIAM EDWIN DYESS: THE BATAAN DEATH MARCH

Captain William Edwin "Ed" Dyess was a 25-year-old from Albany, Texas. While defending the Philippines, he fought bravely for four long months. On April 9, 1942, American and Filipino soldiers were forced to surrender to the Japanese. Dyess became one of more than **70,000** men forced into the Bataan Death March.

April 10, 1942

BATAAN PENINSULA, THE PHILIPPINES

Name?

William Edwin Dyess, captain, U.S. Army Air Forces, serial number O-22526.

Name, rank, and serial number. That's all the Japanese will get out of me.

After our capture, the Japanese began marching us 85 miles (137 kilometers) from Mariveles, Bataan, to San Fernando, Pampanga. Under a blazing tropical sun, our weary feet carried us forward. No sleep. No rest.

Our only goal was to stay alive.

All night long, muzzle flashes and gunshots followed our footsteps.

As the days dragged on, the horror mounted.

Soldiers weak from malaria met the end of a bayonet.

Unconscious men fell beneath the wheels of army trucks.

How can they treat us this way?

After six days without food, we staggered into the prison camp in San Fernando.

But the Japanese had not broken my spirit.

I've got to escape.

We were packed into filthy cells. The death march had been only the beginning of my nightmare.

Almost one year later, I did just that.

Come on! Now is our chance!

While on unguarded work duty, I disappeared into the jungle with nine other Americans and two Filipino soldiers.

Dyess spent weeks on the run before eventually returning to the United States. Upon his return, he rose to the rank of lieutenant colonel.

On December 22, 1943, a training mission turned deadly. Rather than crash his burning plane into a populated area, he guided it to a vacant lot. He died a hero in the process.

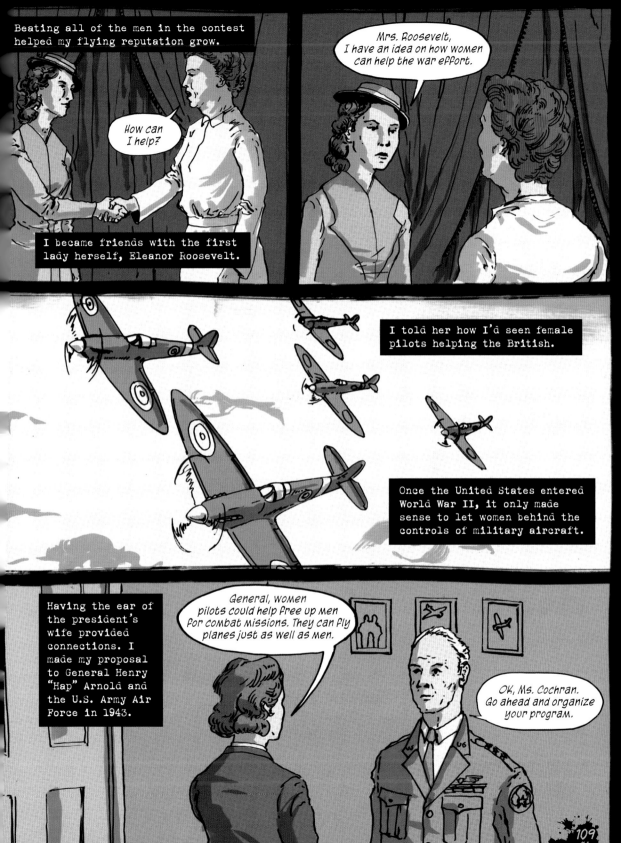

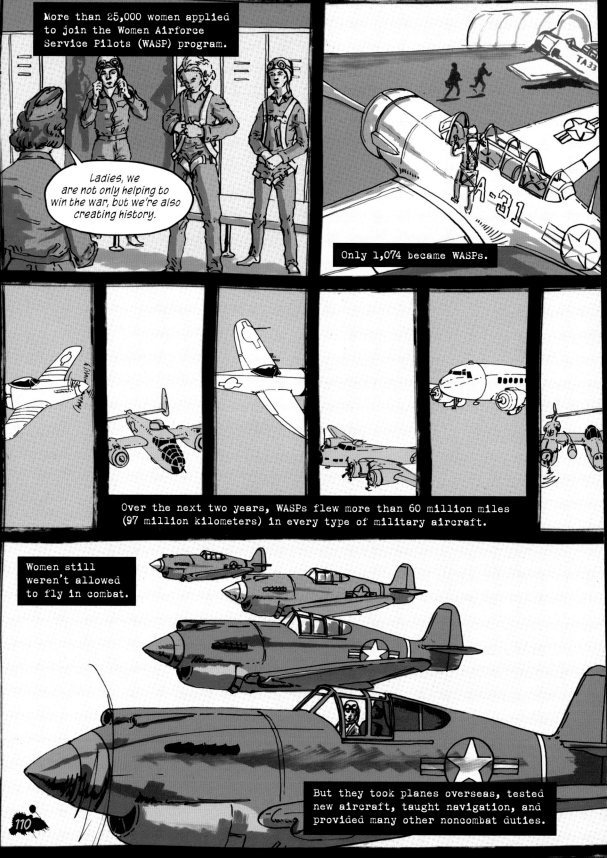

More than 25,000 women applied to join the Women Airforce Service Pilots (WASP) program.

Ladies, we are not only helping to win the war, but we're also creating history.

Only 1,074 became WASPs.

Over the next two years, WASPs flew more than 60 million miles (97 million kilometers) in every type of military aircraft.

Women still weren't allowed to fly in combat.

But they took planes overseas, tested new aircraft, taught navigation, and provided many other noncombat duties.

At the end of World War II, I was awarded the U.S. Distinguished Service Medal.

I asked that General Arnold himself present the honor.

Ms. Cochran, you might be the most stubborn woman I've ever met. But, you're also the bravest.

Thank you, sir. Coming from you, that means a lot.

After the war, Cochran became the first woman to fly faster than the speed of sound. When she died in 1980, she held more speed, altitude, and distance records than any other male or female pilot in the world.

JACKIE'S STAMP

On March 9, 1996, the U.S. Post Office issued a 50-cent stamp commemorating Jacqueline Cochran. The stamp honored her many accomplishments, before, during, and after World War II. The stamp shows a painting of Cochran after winning the 1938 Bendix Air Race.

CHARLES W. LINDBERG: FLAG OVER IWO JIMA

North Dakota native Charles W. Lindberg was a flamethrower operator for the 3rd Platoon, Easy Company, 28th Regiment. Lindberg's platoon fought at the base of Mount Suribachi on the Japanese controlled Pacific island of Iwo Jima. On February 23, 1945, he took part in the first American flag-raising on Iwo Jima.

February 19, 1945
DAY ONE OF THE INVASION

When we hit Iwo Jima, we were expecting a fight—but nothing like the reception we got.

The Japanese had the whole beach under attack. Most of the fire was raining down from Mount Suribachi.

A flamethrower is a valuable weapon, but its range is limited.

In order to push forward, I had to get in close to the enemy.

After we raised the flag, the troops down below started to cheer. We needed that boost of morale. I was never prouder to serve my country than during that moment.

After being wounded by a Japanese sniper on March 1, Lindberg was evacuated from Iwo Jima. He was honorably discharged in 1946. He was awarded the Silver Star for his bravery and the Purple Heart for his wound. Lindberg passed away on June 24, 2007, the last survivor of the first flag-raising on Iwo Jima.

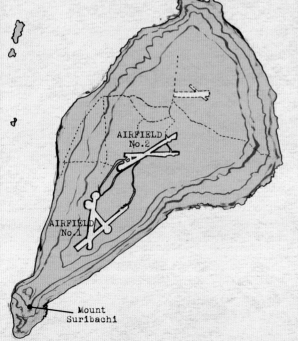

AIRFIELD No. 2

AIRFIELD No. 1

Mount Suribachi

THE IMPORTANCE OF IWO JIMA

The Japanese had two runways in place on Iwo Jima. A third landing strip to the north was incomplete. Controlling these runways on Iwo Jima provided emergency landing spots for damaged U.S. B-29s on their way home after bombing Japan. Ultimately, an estimated 20,000 Allied lives were saved by being able to land on Iwo Jima for repairs. But more than 25,000 men from both sides died in the battle for the island.

Lucie Aubrac: French Freedom Fighter

Lucie Aubrac was a history teacher, a mother, a wife, and a member of the French Resistance. Her husband, Raymond, was an engineer who also secretly worked against the German occupation of France. Aubrac and her husband often helped men on the run from the German secret police escape from France. These skills proved important when Raymond was captured by the Nazis.

October 21, 1943
GESTAPO HEADQUARTERS
LYON, FRANCE

They admitted me as Mademoiselle Ghislaine de Barbentane, an unwed woman who is five months pregnant.

Don't you understand, sir? My honor is at stake!

If you won't take pity on me, pity my poor unborn child.

I didn't know he was a lousy no-good terrorist. He tricked me!

But my identification papers are fake.

My real name is Lucie Aubrac. I'm a member of the French Resistance.

Arranging for our "marriage" is the only way I'd dare be alone in a building filled with Nazis.

Wouldn't you agree?

Aiding a pregnant woman shows how kind and caring the Gestapo can be to those who are loyal.

I shall arrange for a priest. He will marry the two of you in the traitor's cell.

No! No! I don't want my wedding held behind prison bars!

Please, sir, anywhere else but Montluc.

The lieutenant agrees to help, but he could just as easily change his mind.

Luckily, he is good to his word. Raymond is brought to the Gestapo Headquarters.

You didn't know I was pregnant, did you? For the child's sake, you must marry me.

We embrace and I whisper ...

The truck carrying you back to jail will be attacked by friends.

And then they take Raymond away again.

I can only hope the rescue plan will work.

118

I shouldn't be worried.

Resistance members wait for Raymond's trip back.

One shot takes out the driver.

We are on the guards instantly.

Several other prisoners on the truck are also freed.

But I only have eyes for my husband.

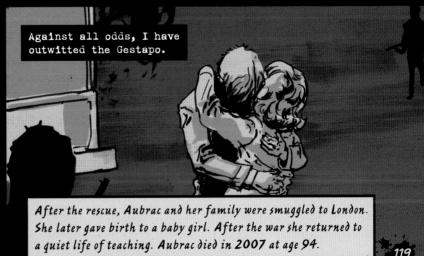

Against all odds, I have outwitted the Gestapo.

After the rescue, Aubrac and her family were smuggled to London. She later gave birth to a baby girl. After the war she returned to a quiet life of teaching. Aubrac died in 2007 at age 94.

LEWIS L. HAYNES: DISASTER AT SEA

Chief Medical Officer Lewis Haynes survived one of the worst naval disasters in U.S. history. Around midnight on July 30, 1945, two Japanese torpedoes struck the USS Indianapolis. About 900 men were believed to have survived the explosion. The horrors that followed the attack ravaged those survivors.

July 30, 1945
THE NORTH PACIFIC OCEAN

So what was the big secret, skipper?

I've never seen things so hush-hush on a mission.

I don't know for sure. Rumor has it we delivered parts for a bomb that could end the war in a matter of days.

Regardless, things were quiet.

The military and their secrets.

Or so I thought.

Doctor, you'd better get life jackets on your patients—now!

I made it to my battle station in the port hanger on the deck. My hands were almost useless, but I was doing my best for the injured.

The warning came too late. We were already sinking.

I ended up in the ocean and swam away from the *Indianapolis* as quickly as possible.

I'd heard stories of survivors being pulled down by the undertow of a sinking ship.

I later heard stories of the terrors from the deep.

There's something biting me!

I never witnessed any attacks.

But others watched helplessly ...

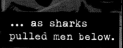

... as sharks pulled men below.

What I did see was some of the strongest men fall completely apart.

There's a Japanese boat over there! They're trying to kill us all!

Calm down, sailor. There's nothing there.

I kept track of the days to hold onto my own sanity.

A U.S. plane finally spotted us on August 2.

Cans of water and life rafts were dropped until help could arrive.

Later that night, the rescue boats finally found us.

Easy, friend. We've got you. You're safe.

Somehow, I managed to stand on my own two feet.

Who are you, sailor?

Doctor Lewis L. Haynes, Chief Medical Officer of the USS *Indianapolis*. What's left of the crew has been stranded in the water for four days.

Stranded in the ocean, Haynes cared for his men as best he could. Many lived due to his leadership. Still, only 317 of the 1,197 men on board the *Indianapolis* survived. After the war, Haynes continued his career in medicine. He even helped develop a way to freeze and save blood for use in blood banks. Haynes died in Florida on March 11, 2001, at age 88.

INDEX

Direct quotations appear on the following pages:

Page 13 from the Declaration of Independence.

Pages 17, 19, 25, 26 from Narratives of the American Revolution by Hugh F. Rankin, ed. (Chicago: R. R. Donnelley & Sons, 1976).

Pages 29, 31 from Diary of Lieutenant Anthony Allaire by Anthony Allaire (New York: New York Times & Arno Press, 1968).

Pages 34, 35 from "Eyewitness Account at Yorktown of Sarah Osborn Benjamin" by David N. Moran, http://www.revolutionarywararchives.org/battles-link/73-eyewitness-account-at-yorktown-of-sarah-osborn-benjamin

Pages 42, 43, 44, 45 from "The First Shot of the Civil War: The Surrender of Fort Sumter, 1861," EyeWitness to History, www.eyewitnesstohistory.com http://www.eyewitnesstohistory.com

Pages 46, 47, 48, 49 from "The First Battle of Bull Run, 1861," EyeWitness to History, http://www.eyewitnesstohistory.com

Pages 50, 51, 52, 53, 54, 55 from "The Battle of the Ironclads, 1862," EyeWitness to History, http://www.eyewitnesstohistory.com

Pages 56, 57, 58, 59 from "Carnage At Antietam, 1862," EyeWitness to History, http://www.eyewitnesstohistory.com

Pages 61, 62, 63 from "Pickett's Charge, 1863," EyeWitness to History, http://www.eyewitnesstohistory.com

Pages 64, 65 from "The Last Stand by Lee's Army," by General John B. Gordon, http://www.historycentral.com/CivilWar/Surrender/Surrendergoron.html

Pages 73, 74, 75 from A Student in Arms by Donald Hankey (New York: E.P. Dutton & Co., 1917).

Page 80 from Letters and Diary of Alan Seeger by Alan Seeger (New York: C. Scribner's Sons, 1917).

Page 83 from Poems by Alan Seeger (New York: C. Scribner's Sons, 1916).

Pages 86-87 from "The Diary of Alvin York" by Alvin York, http://acacia.pair.com/Acacia.Vignettes/The.Diary.of.Alvin.York.html

Page 94 from Over the Top by Arthur Guy Empey (New York: G.P. Putnam's Sons, 1917).